The Complete Works Of Artemus Ward

Part 3: Stories And Romances

by

Artemus Ward

Double9 BOOKS

The Complete Works Of Artemus Ward
Part 3: Stories And Romances
by Artemus Ward

ISBN: 978-93-75552-89-5

Published by

DOUBLE 9 BOOKS

2/13-B, Ansari Road
Daryaganj, New Delhi – 110002
info@double9books.com
www.double9books.com
Tel. 011-40042856

ABOUT THE AUTHOR

Charles Farrar Browne was an American humor writer whose influence helped shape early comic performance through a blend of literary wit and stage presence. Born on 26 April 1834 in Waterford, Maine, he developed a distinctive comedic style that later became associated with his widely recognized persona, Artemus Ward. This character, portrayed as an illiterate yet shrewd figure with Yankee common sense, allowed Browne to comment on society with subtle irony and exaggerated sincerity, creating a form of humor that resonated deeply with audiences. His public performances made him one of the earliest figures to adopt a style now linked to stand-up comedy, earning him recognition as America's first stand-up comedian. Browne's career included extensive touring and writing, where he blended storytelling with satire in a way that showcased his keen observation of social behavior. His success extended beyond the United States, allowing him to reach audiences in the United Kingdom, where he continued to perform until his death on 6 March 1867 in Southampton. He was laid to rest at Kensal Green Cemetery in London, leaving behind a legacy that influenced generations of American humorists.

CONTENTS

PART III
STORIES AND ROMANCES

3.1. MOSES THE SASSY; OR, THE DISGUISED DUKE

CHAPTER I.—ELIZY.

My story opens in the classic presinks of Bostin. In the parler of a bloated aristocratic mansion on Bacon street sits a luvly young lady, whose hair is cuvered ore with the frosts of between 17 Summers. She has just sot down to the piany, and is warblin the popler ballad called "Smells of the Notion," in which she tells how, with pensiv thought, she wandered by a C beat shore. The son is settin in its horizon, and its gorjus light pores in a golden meller flud through the winders, and makes the young lady twict as beautiful nor what she was before, which is onnecessary. She is magnificently dressed up in a Berage basque, with poplin trimmins, More Antique, Ball Morals and 3 ply carpeting. Also, considerable gauze. Her dress contains 16 flounders and her shoes is red morocker, with gold spangles onto them. Presently she jumps up with a wild snort, and pressin her hands to her brow, she exclaims: "Methinks I see a voice!"

A noble youth of 27 summers enters. He is attired in a red shirt and black trowsis, which last air turned up over his boots; his hat, which it is a plug, being cockt onto one side of his classical hed. In sooth, he was a heroic lookin person, with a fine shape. Grease, in its barmiest days, near projuced a more hefty cavileer. Gazin upon him admiringly for a spell, Elizy (for that was her name) organized herself into a tabloo, and stated as follers.

"Ha! do me eyes deceive me earsight? Is it some dreams? No, I reckon not! That frame! them store close! those nose! Yes, it is me own, me only Moses!"

He (Moses) folded her to his hart, with the remark that he was "a hunkey boy."

CHAPTER II.—WAS MOSES Of NOBLE BIRTH?

Moses was foreman of Engine Co. No. 40. Forty's fellers had just bin havin an annual reunion with Fifty's fellers, on the day I introjuce Moses to my readers, and Moses had his arms full of trofees, to wit: 4 scalps, 5 eyes, 3 fingers, 7 ears, (which he chawed off) and several half and quarter sections of noses. When the fair Elizy recovered from her delight at meetin Moses, she said:—"How hast the battle gonest? Tell me!"

"We chawed 'em up—that's what we did!" said the bold Moses.

"I thank the gods!" said the fair Elizy. "Thou did'st excellent well. And, Moses," she continnered, layin her hed confidinly agin his weskit, "dost know I sumtimes think thou istest of noble birth?"

"No!" said he, wildly ketchin hold of hisself. "You don't say so!"

"Indeed do I! Your dead grandfather's sperrit comest to me the tother night."

"Oh no, I guess it's a mistake," said Moses.

"I'll bet two dollars and a quarter he did!" replied Elizy. "He said, 'Moses is a Disguised Juke!'"

"You mean Duke," said Moses.

"Dost not the actors all call it Juke?" said she.

That settled the matter.

> "I hav thought of this thing afore," said Moses, abstractedly. "If it is so, then thus it must be! 2 B or not 2 B! Which? Sow, sow! But enuff. O life! life!—YOU'RE TOO MANY FOR ME!" He tore out some of his pretty yeller hair, stampt on the floor sevril times, and was gone.

CHAPTER III.—THE PIRUT FOILED.

Sixteen long and weary years has elapst since the seens narrated in the last chapter took place. A noble ship, the Sary Jane, is a sailin from France to Ameriky via the Wabash Canal. A pirut ship is in hot pursoot of the Sary. The pirut capting isn't a man of much principle and intends to kill all the people on bored the Sary and confiscate the wallerbles. The capting of the S.J. is on the pint of givin in, when a fine lookin feller in russet boots and a buffalo overcoat rushes forored and obsarves:

"Old man! go down stairs! Retire to the starbud bulkhed! I'll take charge of this Bote!"

"Owdashus cuss!" yelled the capting, "away with thee or I shall do mur-rer-der-r-r!"

"Skurcely," observed the stranger, and he drew a diamond-hilted fish-knife and cut orf the capting's hed. He expired shortly, his last words bein, "we are governed too much."

"People!" sed the stranger, "I'm the Juke d'Moses!"

"Old hoss!" sed a passenger, "methinks thou art blowin!" whareupon the Juke cut orf his hed also.

"Oh that I should live to see myself a dead body!" screamed the unfortnit man. "But don't print any verses about my deth in the newspapers, for if you do I'll haunt ye!"

"People!" sed the Juke, "I alone can save you from yon bloody pirut! Ho! a peck of oats!" The oats was brought, and the Juke, boldly mountin the jibpoop, throwed them onto the towpath. The pirut rapidly approached, chucklin with fiendish delight at the idee of increasin his ill-gotten gains. But the leadin hoss of the pirut ship stopt suddent on comin to the oats, and commenst for to devour them. In vain the piruts swore and throwd stones and bottles at the hoss—he wouldn't budge a inch. Meanwhile the Sary Jane, her hosses on the full jump, was fast leavin the pirut ship!

"Onct agin do I escape deth!" sed the Juke between his clencht teeth, still on the jibpoop.

CHAPTER IV. THE WANDERER'S RETURN.

The Juke was Moses the Sassy! Yes, it was!

He had bin to France and now he was home agin in Bostin, which gave birth to a Bunker Hill!! He had some trouble in gitting hisself acknowledged as Juke in France, as the Orleans Dienasty and Borebones were fernest him, but he finally conkered. Elizy knowd him right off, as one of his ears and a part of his nose had bin chawed off in his fights with opposition firemen during boyhood's sunny hours. They lived to a green old age, beloved by all, both grate and small. Their children, of which they have numerous, often go up onto the Common and see the Fountain squirt.

This is my 1st attempt at writin a Tail & it is far from bein perfeck, but if I have indoosed folks to see that in 9 cases out of 10 they can either make life as barren as the Desert of Sarah, or as joyyus as a flower garding, my object will have been accomplished, and more too.

3.2. MARION: A ROMANCE OF THE FRENCH SCHOOL

I.

—, Friday, —, 1860.

On the sad sea shore! Always to hear the moaning of these dismal waves!

Listen. I will tell you my story—my story of love, of misery, of black despair.

I am a moral Frenchman.

She whom I adore, whom I adore still, is the wife of a fat Marquis—a lop-eared, blear-eyed, greasy Marquis. A man without soul. A man without sentiment, who cares naught for moonlight and music. A low, practical man, who pays his debts. I hate him.

II.

She, my soul's delight, my empress, my angel, is superbly beautiful.

I loved her at first sight—devotedly, madly.

She dashed past me in her coupe. I saw her but a moment—perhaps only an instant—but she took me captive then and there, forevermore.

Forevermore!

I followed her, after that, wherever she went. At length she came to notice, to smile upon me. My motto was en avant! That is a French word. I got it out of the back part of Worcester's Dictionary.

III.

She wrote me that I might come and see her at her own house. Oh, joy, joy unutterable, to see her at her own house!

I went to see her after nightfall, in the soft moonlight.

She came down the graveled walk to meet me, on this beautiful midsummer night—came to me in pure white, her golden hair in splendid disorder—strangely beautiful, yet in tears!

She told me her fresh grievances.

The Marquis, always a despot, had latterly misused her most vilely.

That very morning, at breakfast, he had cursed the fishballs and sneered at the pickled onions.

She is a good cook. The neighbors will tell you so. And to be told by the base Marquis—a man who, previous to his marriage, had lived at the cheap eating-houses—to be told by him that her manner of frying fishballs was a failure—it was too much.

Her tears fell fast. I too wept. I mixed my sobs with her'n.

"Fly with me!" I cried.

Her lips met mine. I held her in my arms. I felt her breath upon my cheek! It was Hunkey.

"Fly with me. To New York! I will write romances for the Sunday papers—real French romances, with morals to them. My style will be appreciated. Shop girls and young mercantile persons will adore it, and I will amass wealth with my ready pen."

Ere she could reply—ere she could articulate her ecstasy, her husband, the Marquis, crept snake-like upon me.

Shall I write it? He kicked me out of the garden—he kicked me into the street.

I did not return. How could I? I, so ethereal, so full of soul, of sentiment, of sparkling originality! He, so gross, so practical, so lop-eared!

Had I returned, the creature would have kicked me again.

So I left Paris for this place—this place, so lonely, so dismal.

Ah me!

Oh dear!

3.3. A ROMANCE.—WILLIAM BARKER, THE YOUNG PATRIOT

I.

"No, William Barker, you cannot have my daughter's hand in marriage until you are her equal in wealth and social position."

The speaker was a haughty old man of some sixty years, and the person whom he addressed was a fine-looking young man of twenty-five.

With a sad aspect the young man withdrew from the stately mansion.

II.

Six months later the young man stood in the presence of the haughty old man.

"What! YOU here again?" angrily cried the old man.

"Ay, old man," proudly exclaimed William Barker. "I am here, your daughter's equal and yours?"

The old man's lips curled with scorn. A derisive smile lit up his cold features; when, casting violently upon the marble center table an enormous roll of greenbacks, William Barker cried—

"See! Look on this wealth. And I've tenfold more! Listen, old man! You spurned me from your door. But I did not despair. I secured a contract for furnishing the Army of the — with beef—"

"Yes, yes!" eagerly exclaimed the old man.

"—and I bought up all the disabled cavalry horses I could find—"

"I see! I see!" cried the old man. "And good beef they make, too."

"They do! they do! and the profits are immense."

"I should say so!"

"And now, sir, I claim your daughter's fair hand!"

"Boy, she is yours. But hold! Look me in the eye. Throughout all this have you been loyal?"

"To the core!" cried William Barker.

"And," continued the old man, in a voice husky with emotion, "are you in favor of a vigorous prosecution of the war?"

"I am, I am!"

"Then, boy take her! Maria, child, come hither. Your William claims thee. Be happy, my children! And whatever our lot in life may be, LET US ALL SUPPORT THE GOVERNMENT!"

3.4. A ROMANCE—THE CONSCRIPT

[Which may bother the reader a little unless he is familiar with the music of the day.]

CHAPTER I.

Philander Reed struggled with spool-thread and tape in a dry- goods store at Ogdensburg, on the St. Lawrence River, State of New York. He Rallied Round the Flag, Boys, and HAILED Columbia every time she passed that way. One day a regiment returning from the war Came Marching Along, bringing An Intelligent Contraband with them, who left the South about the time Babylon was a-Fallin', and when it was apparent to all well-ordered minds that the Kingdom was Coming, accompanied by the Day of Jubilee. Philander left his spool-thread and tape, rushed into the street, and by his Long-Tail Blue, sed, "Let me kiss him for his Mother." Then, with patriotic jocularity, he inquired, "How is your High Daddy in the Morning?" to which Pomp of Cudjo's Cave replied, "That poor Old Slave has gone to rest, we ne'er shall see him more! But U.S.G. is the man for me, or Any other Man." Then he Walked Round.

"And your Master," sed Philander, "where is he?"

"Massa's in the cold, cold ground—at least I hope so!" sed the gay contraband.

"March on, March on! all hearts rejoice!" cried the Colonel, who was mounted on a Bob-tailed nag—on which, in times of Peace, my soul, O Peace! he had betted his money.

"Yaw," sed a German Bold Sojer Boy, "we don't-fights-mit-Segel as much as we did."

The regiment marched on, and Philander betook himself to his mother's Cottage Near the Banks of that Lone River, and rehearsed the stirring speech he was to make that night at a war meeting.

"It's just before the battle, Mother," he said, "and I want to say something that will encourage Grant."

CHAPTER II.—MABEL.

Mabel Tucker was an orphan. Her father, Dan Tucker, was run over one day by a train of cars though he needn't have been, for the kind-hearted engineer told him to Git out of the Way.

Mabel early manifested a marked inclination for the milinery business, and at the time we introduce her to our readers she was Chief Engineer of a Millinery Shop and Boss of a Sewing Machine.

Philander Reed loved Mabel Tucker, and Ever of her was Fondly Dreaming; and she used to say, "Will you love me Then as Now?" to which he would answer that he would, and WITHOUT the written consent of his parents.

She sat in the parlor of the Cot where she was Born, one Summer's eve, with pensive thought, when Somebody came Knocking at the Door. It was Philander. Fond Embrace and things. Thrilling emotions. P. very pale and shaky in the legs. Also, sweaty.

"Where hast thou been?" she sed. "Hast been gathering shells from youth to age, and then leaving them like a che-eild? Why this tremors? Why these Sadfulness?"

> "Mabeyuel!" he cried. "Mabeyuel! They've Drafted me
> into the Army!"

An orderly Surgeant now appears and says, "Come, Philander, let's be a-marching;" And he tore her from his embrace (P.'s) and marched the conscript to the Examining Surgeon's office.

> Mabel fainted in two places. It was worse than Brother's
> Fainting at the Door.

CHAPTER III.—THE CONSCRIPT.

Philander Reed hadn't three hundred dollars, being a dead-broken Reed, so he must either become one of the noble Band who are Coming, Father Abraham, three hundred thousand more, or skedaddle across the St. Lawrence River to the Canada Line. As his opinions had recently undergone a radical change, he chose the latter course, and was soon Afloat, afloat, on the swift rolling tide. "Row, brothers, row," he cried, "the stream runs fast, the Sergeant is near, and the Zamination's past, and I'm a able- bodied man."

Landing, he at once imprinted a conservative kiss on the Canada Line, and feelingly asked himself, "Who will care for Mother now? But I propose to stick it out on this Line if it takes all Summer."

CHAPTER IV.—THE MEETING.

It was evening, IT was. The Star of the Evening, Beautiful Star, shone brilliantly, adorning the sky with those "Neutral" tints which have characterized all British skies ever since this War broke out.

Philander sat on the Canada Line, playing with his Yard-stick, and perhaps about to take the measure of an unmade piece of calico; when Mabel, with a wild cry of joy, sprang from a small boat to his side. The meeting was too much. They divided a good square faint between them this time. At last Philander found his utterance, and said, "Do they think of me at Home, do they ever think of me?"

"No," she replied, "but they do at the recruiting office."

"Ha! 'tis well."

"Nay, dearest," Mabel pleaded, "come home and go to the war like a man! I will take your place in the Dry Goods store. True, a musket is a little heavier than a yardstick, but isn't it a rather more manly weapon?"

"I don't see it," was Philander's reply; "besides, this war isn't conducted accordin' to the Constitution and Union. When it is— when it is, Mabeyuel, I will return and enlist as a Convalescent!"

"Then, sir," she said, with much American disgust in her countenance, "then, sir, farewell!"

"Farewell!" he said, "and When this Cruel War is Over, pray that we may meet again!"

"Nary!" cried Mabel, her eyes flashing warm fire,—"nary. None but the Brave deserve the Sanitary Fair! A man who will desert his country in its hour of trial would drop Faro checks into the Contribution Box on Sunday. I hain't got time to tarry—I hain't got time to stay!—but here's a gift at parting: a White Feather: wear it in your hat!" and She was Gone from his gaze, like a beautiful dream.

Stung with remorse and mosquitoes, this miserable young man, in a fit of frenzy, unsheathed his glittering dry-goods scissors, cut off four yards (good measure) of the Canada Line, and hanged himself on a Willow Tree. Requiescat in Tape. His stick drifted to My Country, 'tis of thee! And may be seen, in connection with many others, on the stage of any New York theatre every night.

The Canadians won't have any line pretty soon. The skedaddlers will steal it. Then the Canadians won't know whether they're in the United States or not, in which case they may be drafted.

Mabel married a Brigadier-General, and is happy.

3.5. A ROMANCE—ONLY A MECHANIC

In a sumptuously furnished parlor in Fifth Avenue, New York, sat a proud and haughty belle. Her name was Isabel Sawtelle. Her father was a millionaire, and his ships, richly laden, ploughed many a sea.

By the side of Isabel Sawtelle sat a young man with a clear, beautiful eye, and a massive brow.

"I must go," he sed, "the foreman will wonder at my absence."

"The FOREMAN?" asked Isabel in a tone of surprise.

"Yes, the foreman of the shop where I work."

"Foreman—shop—WORK! What! do YOU work."

"Aye, Miss Sawtelle! I am a cooper!" and his eyes flashed with honest pride.

"What's that?" she asked; "it is something about barrels, isn't it!"

"It is!" he said, with a flashing nostril. "And hogsheads."

"Then go!" she said in a tone of disdain—"go AWAY!"

"Ha!" he cried, "you spurn me, then, because I am a mechanic. Well, be it so! though the time will come, Isabel Sawtelle," he added, and nothing could exceed his looks at this moment—"when you will bitterly remember the cooper you now so cruelly cast off? FAREWELL!"

Years rolled on. Isabel Sawtelle married a miserable aristocrat, who recently died of delirium tremens. Her father failed, and is now a raving maniac, and wants to bite little children. All her brothers (except one) were sent to the penitentiary for burglary, and her mother peddles clams that are stolen for her by little George, her only son that has his freedom. Isabel's sister Bianca rides an immoral spotted horse in the circus, HER husband having long since been hanged for murdering his own uncle on his mother's side. Thus we see that it is always best to marry a mechanic.

3.6. ROBERTO THE ROVER:—A TALE OF SEA AND SHORE

CHAPTER I.—FRANCE.

Our story opens in the early part of the year 17—. France was rocking wildly from centre to circumference. The arch despot and unscrupulous man, Richard the III., was trembling like an aspen leaf upon his throne. He had been successful, through the valuable aid of Richelieu and Sir. Wm. Donn, in destroying the Orleans Dysentery, but still he trembled? O'Mulligan, the snake-eater of Ireland, and Schnappsgoot of Holland, a retired dealer in gin and sardines, had united their forces—some nineteen men and a brace of bull pups in all—and were overtly at work, their object being to oust the tyrant. O'Mulligan was a young man between fifty-three years of age and was chiefly distinguished for being the son of his aunt on his great grandfather's side. Schnappsgoot was a man of liberal education, having passed three weeks at Oberlin College. He was a man of great hardihood, also, and would frequently read an entire column of "railway matters" in the "Cleveland Herald" without shrieking with agony.

CHAPTER II.—THE KING.

The tyrant Richard the III. (late Mr. Gloster) sat upon his throne in the Palace d' St. Cloud. He was dressed in his best clothes, and gorgeous trappings surrounded him everywhere. Courtiers, in glittering and golden armor, stood ready at his beck. He sat moodily for a while, when suddenly his sword flashed from its silver scabbard, and he shouted—

"Slaves, some wine, ho!"

The words had scarcely escaped his lips ere a bucket of champagne and a hoe were placed before him.

As the king raised the bucket to his lips, a deep voice near by, proceeding from the mouth of the noble Count Staghisnibs, cried— "Drink hearty, old feller."

"Reports traveling on lightning-wings, whisper of strange goings on and cuttings up throughout this kingdom. Knowest thou aught of these things, most noble Hellitysplit?" and the king drew from the upper pocket of his gold-faced vest a paper of John Anderson's solace and proceeded to take a chaw.

"Treason stalks monster-like throughout unhappy France, my liege!" said the noble Hellitysplit. "The ranks of the P.Q.R.'s are daily swelling, and the G.R.J.A.'s are constantly on the increase. Already the peasantry scout at cat-fish, and demand pickled salmon for their noonday repasts. But, my liege," and the brave Hellitysplit eyes flashed fire, "myself and sword are at thy command?"

"Bully for you, Count," said the king. "But soft: methinks report—perchance unjustly—hast spoken suspiciously of thee, most Royal d'Sardine? How is this? Is it a newspaper yarn? WHAT'S UP?"

D'Sardine meekly approached the throne, knelt at the king's feet, and said: "Most patient, gray, and red-headed skinner; my very approved skin-plaster: that I've been asked to drink by the P.Q.R.'s, it is most true, true I have imbibed sundry mugs of lager with them. The very head and front of my offending hath this extent, no more."

"'Tis well!" said the King, rising and looking fiercely around. "Hadst thou proved false I would with my own good sword have cut off yer head, and spilled your ber-lud all over the floor! If I wouldn't, blow me!"

CHAPTER III.—THE ROVER.

Thrilling as the scenes depicted in the preceding chapter indubitably were, those of this are decidedly THRILLINGER. Again are we in the mighty presence of the King, and again is he surrounded by splendour and gorgeously-mailed courtiers. A sea-faring man stands before him. It is Roberto the Rover, disguised as a common sailor.

"So," said the King, "thou wouldst have audience with me!"

"Aye aye, yer 'onor," said the sailor, "just tip us yer grapplin irons and pipe all hands on deck. Reef home yer jib poop and splice yer main topsuls. Man the jibboom and let fly yer top-gallunts. I've seen some salt water in my days, yer land lubber, but shiver my timbers if I hadn't rather coast among seagulls than landsharks. My name is Sweet William. You're old Dick the Three. Ahoy! Awast! Dam my eyes!" and Sweet William pawed the marble floor and swung his tarpaulin after the manner of sailors on the stage, and consequently not a bit like those on shipboard.

"Mariner," said the King, gravely, "thy language is exceeding lucid, and leads me to infer that things is workin' bad."

"Aye, aye, my hearty!" yelled Sweet William, in dulcet strains, reminding the King of the "voluptuous smell of physic," spoken of by the late Mr. Byron.

"What wouldst thou, seafaring man?" asked the King.

"This!" cried the Rover, suddenly taking off his maritime clothing and putting on an expensive suit of silk, bespangled with diamonds. "This! I am Roberto the Rover!"

The King was thunder-struck. Cowering back in his chair of state, he said in a tone of mingled fear and amazement, "Well, may I be gaul-darned!"

"Ber-lud! Ber-lud! Ber-lud!" shrieked the Rover, as he drew a horse-pistol and fired it at the King, who fell fatally killed, his last words being, "WE ARE GOVENRED TOO MUCH—THIS IS THE LAST OF EARTH!!!" At this exciting juncture Messrs. O'Mulligan and Schnappsgoot (who had previously entered into a copartnership with the Rover for the purpose of doing a general killing business) burst into the room and cut off the heads and let out the inwards of all the noblemen they encountered. They then killed themselves and died like heroes, wrapped up in the Star Spangled Banner, to slow music.

FINALE.

The Rover fled. He was captured near Marseilles and thrust into prison, where he lay for sixteen weary years, all attempts to escape being futile. One night a lucky thought struck him. He raised the window and got out. But he was unhappy. Remorse and dyspepsia preyed upon his vitals. He tried Boerhave's Holland Bitters and the Retired Physician's Sands of Life, and got well. He then married the lovely Countess D'Smith, and lived to a green old age, being the triumph of virtue and downfall of vice.

3.7. RED HAND: A TALE OF REVENGE

CHAPTER I.

"Life's but a walking shadow—a poor player."—Shakespeare.

"Let me die to sweet music."—J.W. Shuckers.

"Go forth, Clarence Stanley! Hence to the bleak world, dog! You have repaid my generosity with the blackest ingratitude. You have forged my name on a five thousand dollar check—have repeatedly robbed my money drawer—have perpetrated a long series of high-handed villanies, and now to-night, because, forsooth, I'll not give you more money to spend on your dissolute companions, you break a chair over my aged head. Anyway! You are a young man of small moral principle. Don't ever speak to me again!"

These harsh words fell from the lips of Horace Blinker, one of the merchant princes of New York City. He spoke to Clarence Stanley, his adopted son and a beautiful youth of nineteen summers. In vain did Clarence plead his poverty, his tender age, his inexperience; in vain did he fasten those lustrous blue eyes of his appealingly and tearfully upon Mr. Blinker, and tell him he would make the pecuniary matter all right in the fall, and that he merely shattered a chair over his head by way of a joke. The stony-hearted man was remorseless, and that night Clarence Stanly became a wanderer in the wide, wide world. As he went forth he uttered these words: "H. Blinker, beware! A RED HAND is around, my fine feller!"

CHAPTER. II.

"—a man of strange wild mien—one who has seen trouble."—Sir Walter Scott.

"You ask me, don't I wish to see the Constitution dissolved and broken up. I answer, NEVER, NEVER, NEVER!"—H.W. Faxon.

"They will join our expedition."—Anon.

> "Go in on your muscle."—President Buchanan's instructions to the Collector of Toledo.

"Westward the hoe of Empire Stars its way."—George N. True.

"Where liberty dwells there is my kedentry."—C.R. Dennett.

Seventeen years have become ingulfed in the vast and moist ocean of eternity since the scene depicted in the last chapter occurred. We are in Mexico. Come with me to the Scarlet Banditti's cave. It is night. A tempest is raging tempestuously without, but within we find a scene of dazzling magnificence. The cave is spacious. Chandeliers of solid gold hang up suspended around the gorgeously furnished room, and the marble floor is star-studded with flashing diamonds. It must have cost between two hundred dollars to fit this cave up. It embraced all of the modern improvements. At the head of the cave life-size photographs (by Ryder) of the bandits, and framed in gilt, were hung up suspended. The bandits were seated around a marble table, which was sculped regardless of expense, and were drinking gin and molasses out of golden goblets. When they got out of gin fresh supplies were brought in by slaves from a two-horse wagon outside, which had been captured that day, after a desperate and bloody struggle, by the bandits, on the plains of Buena Vista.

At the head of the table sat the Chief. His features were swarthy but elegant. He was splendidly dressed in new clothes, and had that voluptuous, dreamy air of grandeur about him which would at once rivet the gaze of folks generally. In answer to a highly enthusiastic call he arose and delivered an able and eloquent speech. We regret that our space does not permit us to give this truly great speech in full—we can merely give a synopsis of the distinguished speaker's remarks. "Comrades! listen to your chief. You all know my position on Lecompton. Where I stand in regard to low tolls on the Ohio Canal is equally clear to you, and so with the Central American question. I believe I understand my little Biz. I decline defining my position on the Horse Railroad until after the Spring Election. Whichever way I says I don't say so myself unless I says so also. Comrades! be virtuous and you'll be happy." The Chief sat down amidst great applause, and was immediately presented with an elegant gold headed cane by his comrades, as a slight testimonial of their respect.

CHAPTER III.

"This is the last of Earth."—Page.

> "The hope of America lies in its well-conducted school-houses." —Bone.

"I wish it to be distinctly understood that I want the Union to be Reserved."—N.T. Nash.

> "Sine qua non Ips Dixit Quid pro quo cui bono Ad
> infininim E Unibus plurum."—Brown.

Two hours later. Return we again to the Banditti's Cave. Revelry still holds high carnival among the able and efficient bandits. A knock is heard at the door. From his throne at the head of the table the Chief cries, "Come in!" and an old man, haggard, white-haired, and sadly bent, enters the cave.

"Messieurs," he tremblingly ejaculates, "for seventeen years I have not tasted of food!"

"Well," says a kind-hearted bandit, "if that's so I expect you must be rather faint. We'll get you up a warm meal immediately, stranger."

"Hold!" whispered the Chief in tones of thunder, and rushing slowly to the spot; "this is about played out. Behold in me RED HAND, the Bandit Chief, once Clarence Stanley, whom you cruelly turned into a cold world seventeen years ago this very night! Old man, perpare to go up!" Saying which the Chief drew a sharp carving knife and cut off Mr. Blinker's ears. He then scalped Mr. B., and cut all of his toes off. The old man struggled to extricate himself from his unpleasant situation, but was unsuccessful.

"My goodness," he piteously exclaimed, "I must say you are pretty rough. It seems to me—."

This is all of this intensely interesting tale that will be published in the "Plain Dealer." The remainder of it may be found in the great moral family paper, "The Windy Flash" published in New York by Stimpkins. "The Windy Flash" circulates 4,000,000 copies weekly.

IT IS THE ALL-FIREDEST PAPER EVER PRINTED. IT IS THE ALL-FIREDEST PAPER EVER PRINTED. IT IS THE ALL-FIREDEST PAPER EVER PRINTED. IT IS THE ALL-FIREDEST PAPER EVER PRINTED.

IT'S THE CUSSEDEST BEST PAPER IN THE WORLD. IT'S THE CUSSEDEST BEST PAPER IN THE WORLD. IT'S THE CUSSEDEST BEST PAPER IN THE WORLD. IT'S THE CUSSEDEST BEST PAPER IN THE WORLD.

IT'S A MORAL PAPER. IT'S A MORAL PAPER. IT'S A MORAL PAPER. IT'S A MORAL PAPER.

SOLD AT ALL THE CORNER GROCERIES. SOLD AT ALL THE CORNER GROCERIES. SOLD AT ALL THE CORNER GROCERIES. SOLD AT ALL THE CORNER GROCERIES.

3.8. PYROTECHNY: A ROMANCE AFTER THE FRENCH.

I.—THE PEACEFUL HAMLET.

Nestling among the grand hills of New Hampshire, in the United States of America, is a village called Waterbury.

Perhaps you were never there.

I do not censure you if you never were.

One can get on very well without going to Waterbury.

Indeed, there are millions of meritorious persons who were never there, and yet they are happy.

In this peaceful hamlet lived a young man named Pettingill.

Reuben Pettingill.

He was an agriculturist.

A broad-shouldered, deep-chested agriculturist.

He was contented to live in this peaceful hamlet.

He said it was better than a noisy Othello.

Thus do these simple children of nature joke in a first class manner.

II.—MYSELF.

I write this romance in the French style.

Yes: something that way.

The French style consists of making just as many paragraphs as possible.

Thus one may fill up a column in a very short time.

I am paid by the column, and the quicker I can fill up a column— but this is a matter to which we will not refer.

We will let this matter pass.

III.—PETTINGILL.

Reuben Pettingill was extremely industrious.

He worked hard all the year round on his father's little farm.

Right he was!

Industry is a very fine thing.

It is one of the finest things of which we have any knowledge.

Yet do not frown, "do not weep for me," when I state that I don't like it.

It doesn't agree with me.

I prefer indolence.

I am happiest when I am idle.

I could live for months without performing any kind of labour, and at the expiration of that time I should feel fresh and vigorous enough to go right on in the same way for numerous more months.

This should not surprise you.

Nothing that a modern novelist does should excite astonishment in any well-regulated mind.

IV.—INDEPENDENCE DAY.

The 4th of July is always celebrated in America with guns, and processions, and banners, and all those things.

You know why we celebrate this day.

The American Revolution, in 1775, was perhaps one of the finest revolutions that was ever seen. But I have not time to give you a full history of the American Revolution. It would consume years to do it, and I might weary you.

One 4th of July Reuben Pettingill went to Boston.

He saw great sights.

He saw the dense throng of people, the gay volunteers, the banners, and, above all, he saw the fireworks.

I despise myself for using so low a word, but the fireworks "licked" him.

A new world was opened to this young man.

He returned to his parents and the little farm among the hills, with his heart full of fireworks.

He said, "I will make some myself."

He said this while eating a lobster on top of the coach.

He was an extraordinary skilful young man in the use of a common clasp-knife.

With that simple weapon he could make, from soft wood, horses, dogs, cats, etc. He carved excellent soldiers also.

I remember his masterpiece.

It was "Napoleon crossing the Alps."

> Looking at it critically, I should say it was rather short of Alps.

An Alp or two more would have improved it; but, as a whole, it was a wonderful piece of work; and what a wonderful piece of work is a wooden man, when his legs and arms are all right.

V.—WHAT THIS YOUNG MAN SAID.

He said, "I can make just as good fireworks as them in Boston."

"Them" was not grammatical, but why care for grammar as long as we are good?

VI.—THE FATHER'S TEARS.

Pettingill neglected the farm.

He said that it might till itself—he should manufacture some gorgeous fireworks, and exhibit them on the village green on the next 4th of July.

He said the Eagle of Fame would flap his wings over their humble roof ere many months should pass away.

"If he does," said old Mr. Pettingill, "we must shoot him and bile him, and eat him, because we shall be rather short of meat, my son, if you go on in this lazy way."

And the old man wept.

He shed over 120 gallons of tears.

That is to say, a puncheon. But by all means let us avoid turning this romance into a farce.

VII.—PYROTECHNY.

But the headstrong young man went to work, making fireworks.

He bought and carefully studied a work on pyrotechny.

The villagers knew that he was a remarkably skilful young man, and they all said, "We shall have a great treat next 4th of July."

Meanwhile Pettingill worked away.

VIII.—THE DAY.

The great day came at last.

Thousands poured into the little village from far and near.

There was an oration, of course.

IX.—ORATORY IN AMERICA.

Yes; there was an oration.

We have a passion for oratory in America—political oratory chiefly.

Our political orators never lose a chance to "express their views."

They will do it. You cannot stop them.

There was an execution in Ohio one day, and the Sheriff, before placing the rope round the murderer's neck, asked him if he had any remarks to make?

"If he hasn't," said a well-known local orator, pushing his way rapidly through the dense crowd to the gallows—"if our ill-starred feller-citizen don't feel inclined to make a speech and is in no hurry, I should like to avail myself of the present occasion to make some remarks on the necessity of a new protective tariff!"

X.—PETTINGILL'S FIREWORKS.

As I said in Chapter VIII., there was an oration. There were also processions, and guns, and banners.

"This evening," said the chairman of the committee of arrangements, "this evening, fellow-citizens, there will be a grand display of fireworks on the village green, superintended by the inventor and manufacturer, our public-spirited townsman, Mr. Reuben Pettingill."

Night closed in, and an immense concourse of people gathered on the village green.

On a raised platform, amidst his fireworks, stood Pettingill.

He felt that the great hour of his life had come, and, in a firm, clear voice, he said:

"The fust fireworks, feller-citizens, will be a rocket, which will go up in the air, bust, and assume the shape of a serpint."

He applied a match to the rocket, but instead of going up in the air, it flew wildly down into the grass, running some distance with a hissing kind of sound, and causing the masses to jump round in a very insane manner.

Pettingill was disappointed, but not disheartened. He tried again.

"The next fireworks," he said, "will go up in the air, bust, and become a beautiful revolvin' wheel."

But alas! it didn't. It only ploughed a little furrow in the green grass, like its unhappy predecessor.

The masses laughed at this, and one man—a white-haired old villager—said, kindly but firmly, "Reuben, I'm 'fraid you don't understand pyrotechny."

Reuben was amazed. Why did his rockets go down instead of up? But, perhaps, the others would be more successful, and, with a flushed face, and in a voice scarcely as firm as before, he said:

"The next specimen of pyrotechny will go up in the air, bust, and become an eagle. Said eagle will soar away into the western skies, leavin' a red trail behind him as he so soars."

But, alas! again. No eagle soared, but, on the contrary, that ordinary proud bird buried its head in the grass.

The people were dissatisfied. They made sarcastic remarks. Some of them howled angrily. The aged man who had before spoken said, "No, Reuben, you evidently don't understand pyrotechny."

Pettingill boiled with rage and disappointment.

"You don't understand pyrotechny!" the masses shouted.

Then they laughed in a disagreeable manner, and some unfeeling lads threw dirt at our hero.

"You don't understand pyrotechny!" the masses yelled again.

> "Don't I?" screamed Pettingill, wild with rage; "don't
> you think I do?"

Then seizing several gigantic rockets he placed them over a box of powder, and touched the whole off.

THIS rocket went up. It did, indeed.

There was a terrific explosion.

No one was killed, fortunately; though many were injured.

The platform was almost torn to pieces.

But proudly erect among the falling timbers stood Pettingill, his face flashing with wild triumph; and he shouted: "If I'm any judge of pyrotechny, THAT rocket has went off."

Then seeing that all the fingers on his right hand had been taken close off in the explosion, he added: "And I ain't so dreadful certain but four of my fingers has went off with it, because I don't see 'em here now!"

3.9. THE LAST OF THE CULKINSES

A DUEL IN CLEVELAND—DISTANCE TEN PACES—BLOODY RESULT—FLIGHT OF ONE OF THE PRINCIPALS—FULL PARTICULARS.

A few weeks since a young Irishman name Culkins wandered into Cleveland from New York. He had been in America only a short time. He overflowed with book learning, but was mournfully ignorant of American customs, and as innocent and confiding withal as the Babes in the Wood. He talked much of his family, their commanding position in Connaught,

Ireland, their immense respectability, their chivalry, and all that sort of thing. He was the only representative of that mighty race in this country. "I'm the last of the Culkinses!" he would frequently say, with a tinge of romantic sadness, meaning, we suppose, that he would be the last when the elder Culkins (in the admired language of the classics) "slipped his wind." Young Culkins proposed to teach Latin, Greek, Spanish, Fardown Irish, and perhaps Choctaw, to such youths as desired to become thorough linguists. He was not very successful in this line, and concluded to enter the office of a prominent law firm on Superior Street as a student. He dove among the musty and ponderous volumes with all the enthusiasm of a wild young Irishman, and commenced cramming his head with law at a startling rate. He lodged in the back-room of the office, and previous to retiring he used to sing the favorite ballads of his own Emerald Isle. The boy who was employed in the office directly across the hall used to go to the Irishman's door and stick his ear to the key-hole with a view to drinking in the gushing melody by the quart or perhaps pailful. This vexed Mr. Culkins, and considerably marred the pleasure of the thing, as witness the following:—

"O come to me when daylight sets.

[What yez doing at that door, yer d—d spalpane?]

Sweet, then come to me!

[I'll twist the nose off yez presently, me honey!]

When softly glide our gondolettes

[Bedad, I'll do murther to yez, young gintlemin!]

O'er the moonlit sea."

Of course, this couldn't continue. This, in short, was rather more than the blood of the Culkinses could stand, so the young man, through whose veins such a powerful lot of that blood courses, sprang to the door, seized the eavesdropping boy, drew him within, and commenced to severely chastise him. The boy's master, the gentleman who occupied the office across the hall, here interfered, pulled Mr. Culkins off, thrust him gently against the wall, and slightly choked him. Mr. Culkins bottled his furious wrath for that night, but in the morning he uncorked it and threatened the gentleman (whom for convenience sake we will call Smith) with all sorts of vengeance. He obtained a small horsewhip and tore furiously through the town, on the lookout for Smith.

He sent Smith a challenge, couched in language so scathingly hot that it burnt holes through the paper, and when it reached Smith it was riddled like an old-fashioned milk-strainer. No notice was taken of the challenge, and Culkins' wrath became absolutely terrific. He wrote handbills, which

he endeavoured to have printed, posting Smith as a coward. He wrote a communication for the "New Herald," explaining the whole matter. (This wasn't very rich, we expect.) He urged us to publish his challenge to Smith. Somebody told him that Smith was intending to flee the city in fear on an afternoon train, and Culkins proceeded to the depot, horsewhip in hand, to lie in wait for him. This was Saturday last. During the afternoon Smith concluded to accept the challenge. Seconds and a surgeon were selected, and we are mortified to state that at 10 o'clock in the evening Scanton's Bottom was desecrated with a regular duel. The frantic glee of Culkins when he learned his challenge had been accepted can't be described. Our pen can't do it—a pig-pen couldn't. He wrote a long letter to his uncle in New York, and to his father in Connaught. At about ten o'clock the party proceeded to the field. The moon was not up, the darkness was dense, the ground was unpleasantly moist, and the lights of the town, which gleamed in the distance, only made the scene more desolate and dreary. The ground was paced off and the men arranged. While this was being done, the surgeon, by the light of a dark lantern, arranged his instruments, which consisted of 1 common hand-saw, 1 hatchet, 1 butcher knife, a large variety of smaller knives, and a small mountain of old rag. Neither of the principals exhibited any fear. Culkins insisted that, as the challenging party, he had the right to the word fire. This, after a bitter discussion, was granted. He urged his seconds to place him facing towards the town, so that the lights would be in his favour. This was done without any trouble, the immense benefits of that position not being discovered by Smith's second.

"If I fall," said Culkins to his second, "see me respectably buried and forward bill to Connaught. Believe me, it will be cashed." The arms (horse-pistols) were given to the men, and one of Culkins's seconds said:

"Gentlemen, are you ready?"

SMITH:—Ready.

CULKINS:—Ready. The blood of the Culkinses is aroused!

SECOND:—One, Two, Three—fire!

Culkins's pistol didn't go off. Smith didn't fire.

"That was generous in Smith not to fire," said a second.

"It was inDADE," said Culkins; "I did not think it of the low-lived scoundrel!"

The word was again given. Crack went both pistols simultaneously. The smoke slowly cleared away, and the principals were discovered standing stock-still. The silence and stillness for a moment were awful. No one moved. Soon Smith was seen to reel and then to slowly fall. His second and the surgeon rushed to him. Culkins made a tremendous effort to fly from the field, but was restrained by his seconds.

"The honor of the Culkinses," he roared, "is untarnished—why the divil won't yez let me go? H—ll's blazes, men, will yez be after giving me over to the bailiffs? Docther, Docther!" he shouted, "is he mortally wounded?"

The Doctor said he could not tell—that he was wounded in the shoulder—that a carriage would be sent for and the wounded man taken to his house. Here a heart-rending groan came from Smith, and Culkins, with a Donnybrook shriek, burst from his seconds, knocked over the doctor's lantern, and fled towards the town like greased lightning amidst a chorus of excited voices.

"Hold him!"

"Stop him!"

"Grab him by the coat-tails!"

"Shoot him!"

"Head him off!"

And half of the party started after him at an express-train rate. There was some very fine running indeed. Culkins was brought to a sudden stop against a tall board fence, but he sprang back and cleared it like an English hunter, and tore like a lunatic for the city. Half an hour later the party might have been seen, if it hadn't been so pesky dark, groping blindly around the office in which Culkins had been a student at law.

"Are you here, Culkins?" said one.

"Before Culkins answers that," said a smothered voice in the little room, "tell me who yez are."

"Friends—your seconds!"

"Gintlemin, Culkins is here. The last of the Culkinses is under the bed."

He was dragged out.

"I hope," he said, "the ignoble wretch is not dead, but I call you to witness, gintlemen, that he grossly insulted me."

(We don't care what folks say, but choking a man is a gross insult.—Ed. P.D.)

He was persuaded to retire. There was no danger of his being disturbed that night, as the watch were sleeping sweetly as usual in the big arm-chairs of the various hotels, and he would be able to fly the city in the morning. He had a haggard and worn-out look yesterday morning. Two large bailiffs, he said, had surrounded the building in the night, and he had not slept a wink. And to add to his discomfiture his coat was covered with a variegated and moist mixture, which he thought must be some of the brains of his opponent, they having spattered against him as he passed the dying man in his flight from the field. As Smith was not dead (though the surgeon said he would be confined to his house for several weeks, and there was some danger of mortification setting in), Culkins wisely concluded that the mixture might be something else. A liberal purse was made up for him, and at an early hour yesterday morning the last of the Culkinses went down St. Clair Street on a smart trot. He took this morning's Lakeshore express train at some way-station, and is now on his way to New York. The most astonishing thing about the whole affair is the appearance on the street to-day, apparently well and unhurt, of the gentleman who was so badly "wounded in the shoulder." But a duel was actually "fit."

3.10. A MORMON ROMANCE—REGINALD GLOVERSON

CHAPTER I.—THE MORMON'S DEPARTURE.

> The morning on which Reginald Gloverson was to leave Great Salt Lake City with a mule-train, dawned beautifully.

Reginald Gloverson was a young and thrifty Mormon, with an interesting family of twenty young and handsome wives. His unions had never been blessed with children. As often as once a year he used to go to Omaha, in Nebraska, with a mule-train for goods; but although he had performed the rather perilous journey many times with entire safety, his heart was strangely sad on this particular morning, and filled with gloomy forebodings.

The time for his departure had arrived. The high-spirited mules were at the door, impatiently champing their bits. The Mormon stood sadly among his weeping wives.

"Dearest ones," he said, "I am singularly sad at heart, this morning; but do not let this depress you. The journey is a perilous one, but—pshaw! I have always come back safely heretofore, and why should I fear? Besides, I know that every night, as I lay down on the broad starlit prairie, your bright faces will come to me in my dreams, and make my slumbers sweet and gentle. You, Emily, with your mild blue eyes; and you, Henrietta, with your splendid black hair; and you, Nelly, with your hair so brightly, beautifully golden; and you, Mollie, with your cheeks so downy; and you, Betsy, with your wine-red lips— far more delicious, though, than any wine I ever tasted—and you, Maria, with your winsome voice; and you, Susan, with your—with your—that is to say, Susan, with your—and the other thirteen of you, each so good and beautiful, will come to me in sweet dreams, will you not, Dearestists?"

"Our own," they lovingly chimed, "we will!"

"And so farewell!" said Reginald. "Come to my arms, my own!" he cried, "that is, as many of you as can do it conveniently at once, for I must away."

He folded several of them to his throbbing breast, and drove sadly away.

But he had not gone far when the trace of the off-hind mule became unhitched. Dismounting, he essayed to adjust the trace; but ere he had fairly commenced the task, the mule, a singularly refractory animal—snorted wildly, and kicked Reginald frightfully in the stomach. He arose with difficulty, and tottered feebly towards his mother's house, which was near by, falling dead in her yard, with the remark, "Dear Mother, I've come home to die!"

"So I see," she said; "where's the mules?"

Alas! Reginald Gloverson could give no answer. In vain the heart-stricken mother threw herself upon his inanimate form, crying, "Oh, my son—my son! Only tell me where the mules are, and then you may die if you want to."

In vain—in vain! Reginald had passed on.

CHAPTER II.—FUNERAL TRAPPINGS.

The mules were never found.

Reginald's heart-broken mother took the body home to her unfortunate son's widows. But before her arrival she indiscreetly sent a boy to Bust the news gently to the afflicted wives, which he did by informing them in a hoarse whisper that their "old man had gone in."

The wives felt very badly indeed.

"He was devoted to me," sobbed Emily.

"And to me," said Maria.

"Yes," said Emily, "he thought considerably of you, but not so much as he did of me."

"I say he did!"

"And I say he didn't!"

"He did!"

"He didn't!"

"Don't look at ME, with your squint eyes!"

"Don't shake your red head at ME!"

"Sisters!" said the black-haired Henrietta, "cease this unseemly wrangling. I, as his first wife, shall strew flowers on his grave."

"No you WON'T," said Susan. "I, as his last wife, shall strew flowers on his grave. It's MY business to strew!"

"You shan't, so there!" said Henrietta.

"You bet I will!" said Susan, with a tear-suffused cheek.

"Well, as for me," said the practical Betsy, "I ain't on the Strew, much, but I shall ride at the head of the funeral procession!"

"Not if I've been introduced to myself, you won't," said the golden-haired Nelly; "that's my position. You bet your bonnet- strings it is."

"Children," said Reginald's mother, "you must do some crying, you know, on the day of the funeral; and how many pocket-handkerchers will it take to go round? Betsy, you and Nelly ought to make one do between you."

"I'll tear her eyes out if she perpetrates a sob on my handkercher!" said Nelly.

"Dear daughters in-law," said Reginald's mother, "how unseemly is this anger! Mules is five hundred dollars a span, and every identical mule my poor boy had has been gobbled up by the red man. I knew when my Reginald staggered into the door-yard that he was on the Die, but if I'd only thunk to ask him about them mules ere his gentle spirit took flight, it would have been four thousand dollars in OUR pockets, and NO mistake! Excuse those real tears, but you've never felt a parent's feelin's."

"It's an oversight," sobbed Maria. "Don't blame us!"

CHAPTER III.—DUST TO DUST.

The funeral passed off in a very pleasant manner, nothing occuring to mar the harmony of the occasion. By a happy thought of Reginald's mother, the wives walked to the grave twenty abreast, which rendered that part of the ceremony thoroughly impartial.

That night the twenty wives, with heavy hearts, sought their twenty respective couches. But no Reginald occupied those twenty respective couches—Reginald would never more linger all night in blissful repose in those twenty respective couches—Reginald's head would never more press the twenty respective pillows of those twenty respective couches—never, nevermore!

In another house, not many leagues from the House of Mourning, a gray-haired woman was weeping passionately. "He died," she cried, "he died without sigerfyin', in any respect, where them mules went to!"

CHAPTER IV.—MARRIED AGAIN.

Two years are supposed to elapse between the third and fourth chapters of this original American romance.

A manly Mormon, one evening, as the sun was preparing to set among a select apartment of gold and crimson clouds in the western horizon—although for that matter the sun has a right to "set" where it wants to, and so, I may add has a hen—a manly Mormon, I say, tapped gently at the door of the mansion of the late Reginald Gloverson.

The door was opened by Mrs. Sarah Gloverson.

"Is this the house of the widow Gloverson!" the Mormon asked.

"It is," said Susan.

"And how many is there of she?" inquired the Mormon.

"There is about twenty of her, including me," courteously returned the fair Susan.

"Can I see her?"

"You can."

"Madam," he softly said, addressing the twenty disconsolate widows. "I have seen part of you before! And although I have already twenty-five wives, whom I respect and tenderly care for, I can truly say that I never felt love's holy thrill till I saw thee! Be mine—be mine!" he enthusiastically cried, "and we will show the world a striking illustration of the beauty and truth of the noble lines, only a good deal more so—

> "Twenty-one souls with a single thought, Twenty-one
> hearts that beat as one!"

They were united, they were!

Gentle reader, does not the moral of this romance show that—does it not, in fact, show that however many there may be of a young widow woman, or rather does it not show that whatever number of persons one woman may consist of—well, never mind what it SHOWS. Only this writing Mormon romances is confusing to the intellect. You try it and see.